My Loved One Shines On!

A Gift from Beyond

Disa Van Orman
with Dylan Skye Goedeker

INFINITE OWL PUBLISHING

My Loved One Shines On!

Disa Van Orman

Copies of this book may be purchased at: MyLovedOneShinesOn.com

Cover + Interior design: Rebecca Finkel, F+P Graphic Design
Publisher: Infinite Owl Publishing
Book Consultant: Judith Briles, The Book Shepherd

Library of Congress Catalog Number:
ISBN hard cover: 978-0-9961247-0-6
ISBN soft cover: 978-0-9961247-1-3
ISBN eBook: 978-0-9961247-2-0

Library of Congress Control Number: 2015904865
Categories for cataloging and shelving:
Inspiration | Grieving

10 9 8 7 6 5 4 3 2 1

Printed in Korea by Four Colour Print Group, Louisville, Kentucky

To all of you whose heart is aching

from the loss of a loved one.

May Dylan's words re-ignite a flame of hope and love

and reacquaint you with your laughter, passion and joy.

Oh, you are wrong
if you think I'm gone.

I am right there in your favorite song.

I'm in the sunshine on every morning.

I will come by
without any warning.

All of the sudden, you'll feel me near

and you'll swear that I
whispered right in your ear.

That's me in the hawk
that just flew by

or the breeze in the tree

that catches your eye.

I'll be in your dreams

so you know I'm still here.

You'll wake in the morning
without any fear.

I'll watch over you

wherever you are

at home, at school, or even ... a car.

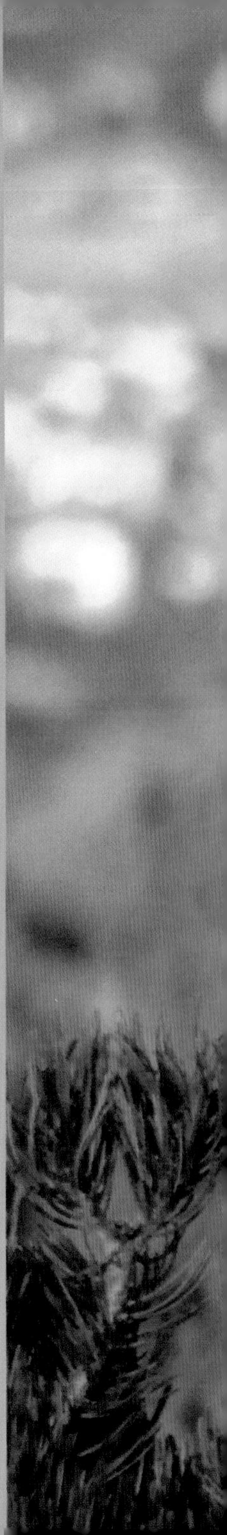

I'm all around you . . .

. . . just listen and feel.

Your body reacts

and you know it's real.

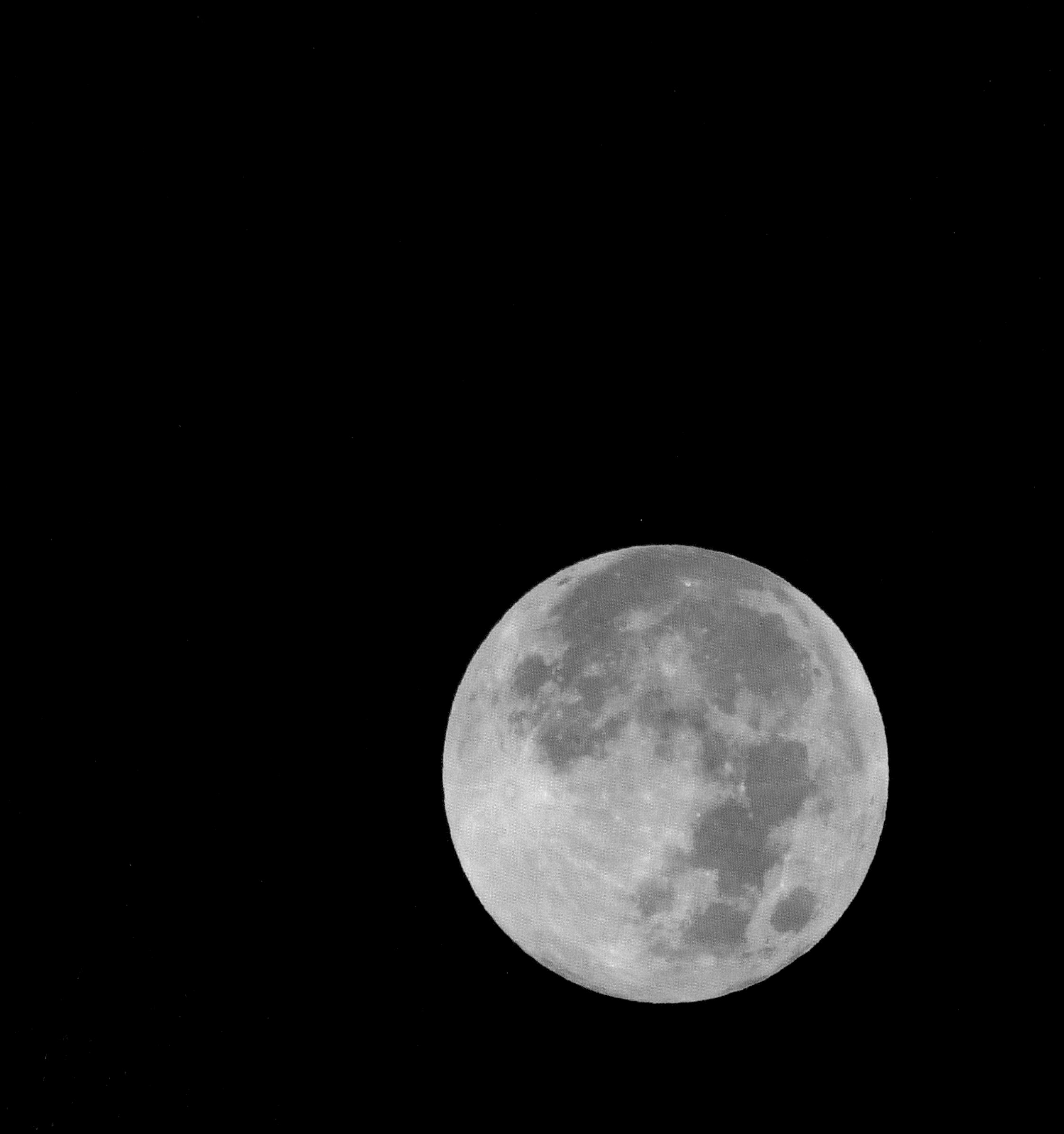

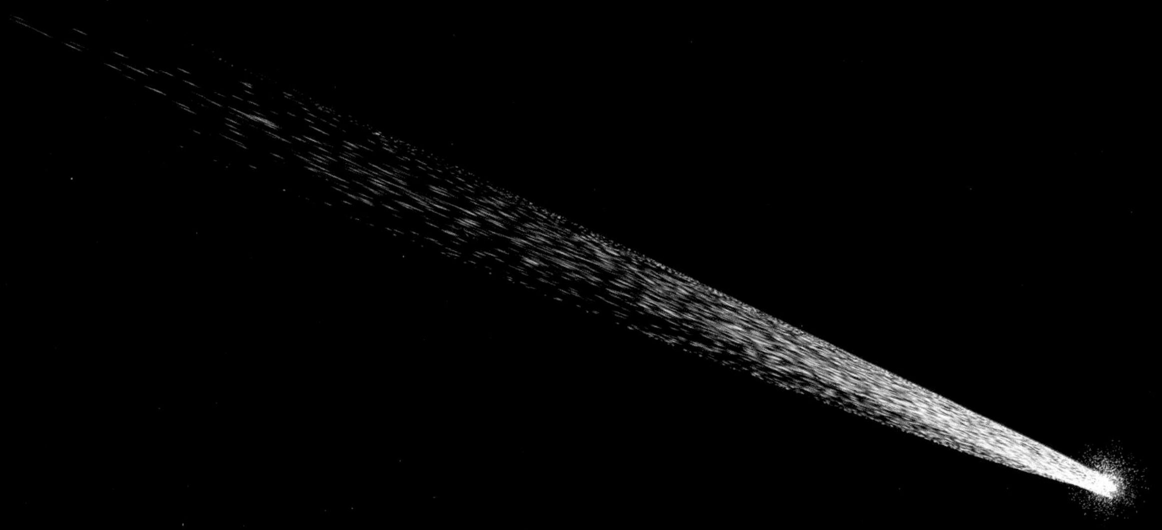

I'll be your shooting star you will see with delight,

to bring you comfort in the middle of the night.

I'll be in a thought, in a word … or a bee.

I'm in the buffalo under a tree.

I'll be in the thunder
or that yellow sunflower.

I'll radiate with my vibrant power.

I will be there when you'll hardly suspect.

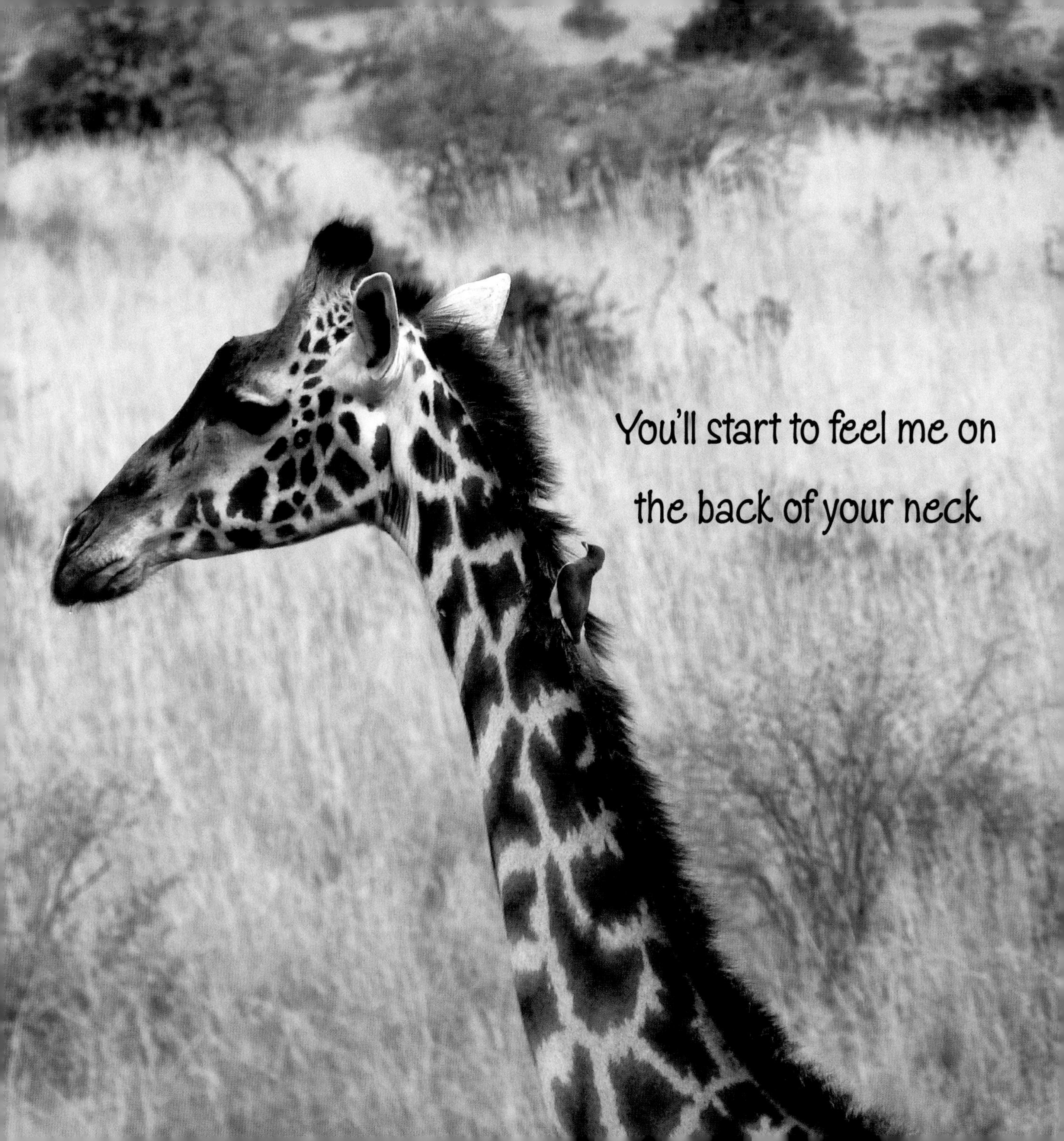
You'll start to feel me on
the back of your neck

And you'll turn and see nothing

but you'll know I am there,

from the feeling of love
that has just filled the air.

I'm in the rainbow high up in the sky,
to help cheer you up if you must cry.

Watch as the
beautiful river does flow.
I love the water,
look at me glow.

You may be looking at some beautiful art,

and you'll know right away that we did not part.

You see you can feel me,

right here in your heart.

In the snow, in the rain, in the sun, and the wind…

always remember that I am your friend.

I'm in the wild, the gentle, the kiss.

Remember these things when it's me that you miss.

I'll bring back fond memories of things

that we shared . . . a dance move,

a smile and
you will know
I still care.

It could be a game, a movie, or even a trip,

that will spread a wide smile all over your lips.

I can bring light
when everything is dark ...

look around and you'll see me, I left a big mark.

All the lives that I touched and my joy will shine on.

Listen . . . I'm the notes in that beautiful song.

Yes everybody, I am right here,

in a tiny small puppy and even the mirror.

I am in you,

as I planted my seed.

I'm in your heart . . .

so there's no need to grieve.

I will live on in your pictures
and stories,

where I am the hero in all of my glory.

There will be many signs

to show I am near,

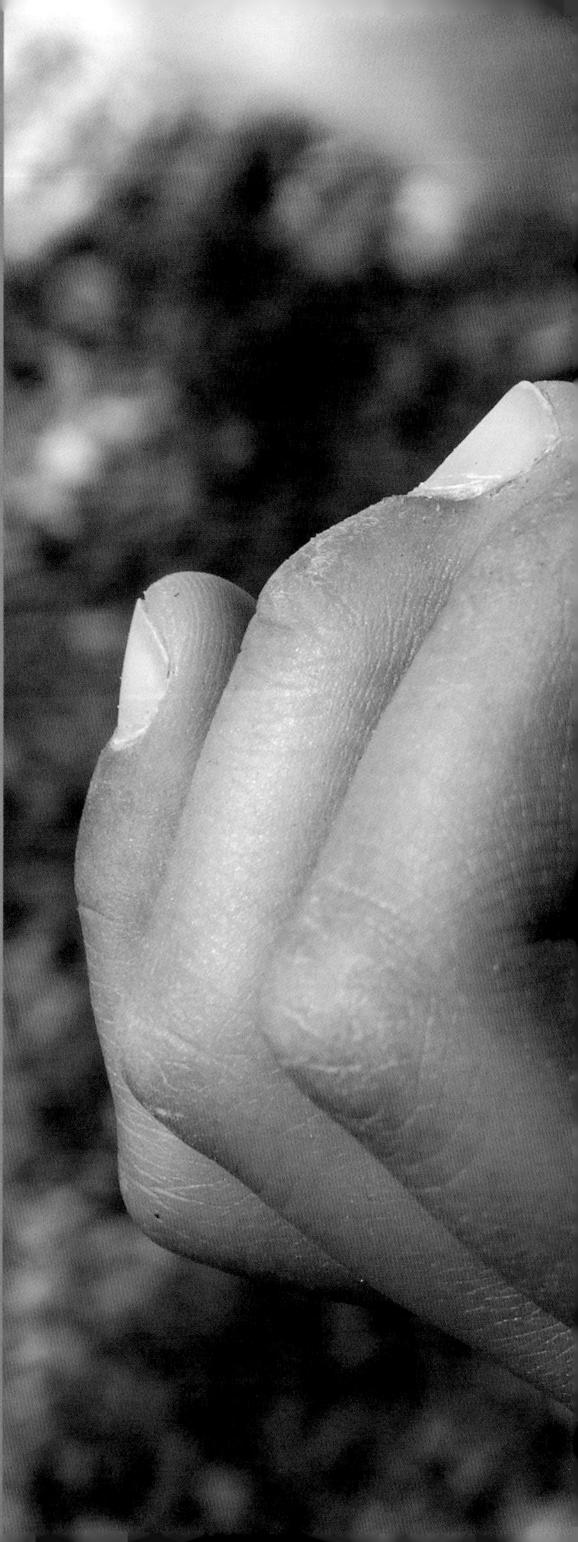

so relax and breathe in

because your loved one is here!

I've filled you with love,
hope, signs and with song.

You see I also know that

MY loved one shines on!

Hey, don't forget

that part about blossom,

because I want this to end with,

"Man … that would be awesome!"

My Loved One Shine On!

Oh, you are wrong if you think I am gone.
I am right there in your favorite song.
I'm in the sunshine on every morning.
I will come by without any warning.

All of the sudden, you'll feel me near
and you'll swear that I whispered right in your ear.
That's me in the hawk that just flew by
or the breeze in the tree that catches your eye.

I'll be in your dreams so you know I'm still here.
You'll wake in the morning without any fear.
I'll watch over you wherever you are
at home, at school or even … a car.

I'm all around you … just listen and feel.
Your body reacts and you know it's real.
I'll be your shooting star you will see with delight,
to bring you comfort in the middle of the night.

I'll be in a thought, in a word … or a bee.
I'm in the buffalo under a tree.
I'll be in the thunder or that yellow sunflower.
I'll radiate with my vibrant power.

I will be there when you'll hardly suspect.
You'll start to feel me on the back of your neck.
And you'll turn and see nothing but you'll know I am there,
from the feeling of love that has just filled the air.

I'm in the rainbow high up in the sky,
to help cheer you up if you must cry.
Watch as the beautiful river does flow.
I love the water, look at me glow.

You may be looking at some beautiful art,
and you'll know right away that we did not part.
You see you can feel me,
right here in your heart.

In the snow, in the rain, in the sun and the wind …
always remember that I am your friend.
I'm in the wild, the gentle, the kiss.
Remember these things when it's me that you miss.

I will bring back fond memories of things that we shared …
a dance move, a smile and you will know I still care.
It could be a game, a movie or even a trip,
that will spread a wide smile all over your lips.

I can bring light when everything is dark …
look around and you'll see me, I left a big mark.
All the lives that I touched and my joy will shine on.
Listen … I'm the notes in that beautiful song.

Yes everybody, I am right here.
In a tiny small puppy and even the mirror.
I am in you, as I planted my seed.
I'm in your heart … so there's no need to grieve.

I will live on in your pictures and stories,
where I am the hero in all of my glory.
There will be many signs to show I am near,
so relax and breathe in because your loved one is here!

I've filled you with love, hope, signs and with song.
You see I also know that MY loved one shines on!
Hey, don't forget that part about blossom,
because I want this to end with "Man … that would be awesome!"

—Dylan Skye Goedeker and Disa Van Orman

Afterword

My whole life changed on that day as I drove to the hospital with Dylan and his mother in the backseat. Suffering from what we thought was the flu, he stop breathing before we could make it to the entrance.

Never again would I be the same person. We had been exposed to the bone with nowhere to turn. I could no longer soothe my family with phrases like, everything will be okay or everything happens for a reason. These words were meaningless.

My healthy, sweet 6-year-old baby was no longer with us. My youngest grandson. We had been traumatized. I could not sleep, eat or even think. This could not be happening to us.

At 4:30 am, I awoke to write the dreadful eulogy. How could I express the feelings I had for someone I totally adored and was lost so young, without a reason or a warning? It seemed impossible to convey Dylan's great joy, with his sparkling personality and his wonderful sense of humor. As rough as any boy, yet so sensitive and loving. Someone whose presence I would seek out in times of sorrow, who could lift me up to my highest high. Someone I craved to laugh, dance, sing and play with. My little love. A little boy who had left his physical body just five days before.

On December 20, 2012 one of the most burdensome tasks lay ahead of me. Amidst this turbulent morning, a weird, wonderful, amazing and unbelievable thing happened. Suddenly, out of the fog of anguish, anger and pain, words begin to clearly come to me. My fingers rapidly typed as I heard them, without thinking or punctuation for fear I would miss something. In less than one half hour, I was done.

I read in amazement. Before my eyes was a poem my little grandson, Dylan, had told me. As I read each word, I thought, what simple beauty. I could understand and feel every word he had said.

What had just taken place? Nothing like this had ever happened to me before in my life. He gave this to me to help us heal and understand that he had evolved or graduated. Dylan had not died. He had managed to pull me from the deepest depths of darkness and light a spark inside my dying heart to help me begin to believe that he had not just disappeared and left.

At times, when I wrestle with this notion, he continues to convince me that this is the truth. Dylan continues to give me words of encouragement and wisdom. I have begun to realize it was and is not so weird or unbelievable. It is wonderful and amazing. We are here to give you hope.

As I tell my story to friends and strangers from all walks of life, more people than I thought, have also experienced a connection to their loved ones who have passed. Within, you will discover Dylan's words. They have been matched to photographs I have taken from my life to portray his feelings. As per his wishes, I am sending this out to all who will listen and understand that your loved ones still shine on and are with you.

Be open and aware of their signs. I was given hope when I no longer had any. We desire this for you now.

Thank you for this everlasting gift my buffalo boy, I love you.

Gebra

About the Authors

Disa Van Orman is Dylan Skye's honored grandmother. She's been renovating houses for nearly 40 years, cofounder of the first dog cleanup service in the nation, Poop Van Scoop, and life caster of humans and animals in cold cast bronze. Around the time Dylan was born, Disa began to take an in-depth intuitive mentoring class. She immediately developed a deep connection with animals, nature and earth, all which is reflected in the exquisite photos she takes from her backyard to the Serengeti.

A Certified Aromatherapist, Healing Touch for Animals Practitioner, Shamanic Practitioner, and a Reiki Master/Teacher. Disa has developed a talent in the art of sacred passing, making the transition period at the end of life as beautiful of a time as possible. Holding a 5th degree belt in Krav Maga, she's an enthusiastic scuba diver, zip liner, repeller, world traveler and photographer, joys she shares with her family.

Since Dylan's passing, she has taken many classes and conferences on intuition, herbology and afterlife. And now an author. Soon to come, more books, classes and speaking to help spread the word and bring comfort to others that their loved ones shine on! Disa lives with her husband and Jack Russell in Denver, Colorado. She enjoys spending as much time as possible with her daughters, son-in law, grandson and granddogs nearby.

Gebra and Dylan

Dylan Skye Goedeker was born in the summer of 2006. He thrived with his mother, father and big brother, who was his best friend. He was quickly known as our sunshine boy. He was so animated, he didn't just talk. Dylan would exude emotion from every part of his body as he danced around and laughed. His favorite color was yellow and he loved his big bird stuffed animal. Athletic, smart, humorous and quite the cuddler, he crammed so much life into his 6 years on Earth. Zip lining in the jungle, playing football, learning sign language, looking forward to his next camping trip, playing lacrosse, swimming with sting rays, delighting in Wii games, cub scouts, and traveling—he did it all with gusto. He continues to spread his humor and love with many of us now. The only thing worse than his passing would have been to never have had him at all.

Acknowledgements

No parent expects to lose a child. Nor does a grandparent. The loss, whether it's one that has been foreshadowed by illness or one that is slammed in suddenly with no warning, tears the heart and soul from those closest. Nothing has shattered my heart like the loss of my grandson.

First and foremost, I must thank my little grandson, Dylan Skye Goedeker, for having trust, guidance and patience with me in getting *My Loved One Shines On!* done. In his six short years with our family, his warmth, silly sense of humor and uncanny wisdom delighted our family and surrounds us, reminding us that his love does shine on

Thank you to my daughter, Aisha Skye, and my son-in-law, Aaron, for allowing me to spend quality time with my grandsons as we built so many memories and a powerful bond that cannot be broken. They and my amazing grandson, Hayden, have been a huge inspiration to me. The Goedeker's have shown me true strength, courage and the power of love. Thank you for allowing me to spread the beautiful gift entrusted to me. Hayden, thank you for continuing to fill my heart with love and laughter and dancing in the moonlight.

Thanks to my patient husband, Bill Van Orman Jr., who took over the businesses, lifted my spirits with his humor, encouraged me to believe in myself and lovingly walked this unknown path with me. I'm grateful to him for including his glorious cape buffalo photo within *My Loved One Shines On!*

Thank you to my daughter, Ashley Sage Van Orman, who gave me confidence to believe in Dylan and myself as I paired favorite photos to his unique words that flowed through to me. She related to my emotions as we shared sad sunglasses moments as we cried and happy times when we told funny stories about Dylan. She shared her gifted hands to reenergize me with Reiki.

My mother Stella Carrillo, who was my best volunteer guinea pig for whatever I was learning. She would lovingly support this endeavor.

Relaxing me with her massages and oils, my sister Freddi Pyrek listened, believed in me, helped me trust and believe in myself and gave me faith to carry on.

My brother Brian Carrillo, who helped me when my computer riled my fury. He also made me realize it was not about convincing someone to believe my experience but to believe in myself and get Dylan's message out to help others who are open and willing.

Friends, what would I have done without them? Especially Dave and Patricia Derby and Lisle Tate-Vonduyke, who had previously lost a child and who unselfishly shared their first hand advice, experience, pain, hope and encouragement. They bared their souls to share their raw emotions to let me know I was not alone and could get through this too. Thank you.

My friends who stayed by my side and kept in contact even when I didn't have the energy to—thank you Birgit Laramie, Trina Zaragoza and Cinda Kennedy. Warming my heart, Roxie Kindsfather-Behunin and Ryan Bonnie Thompson, my very old friends who uplifted me. Teryn Tobin Webster and Mitch Giddens dropped their lives to assist Dylan's family in a vulnerable time. Kelli, Tom, Ben and Ava Loveland who take such great care of them and have also become part of our family. It gave me great comfort and allowed me to put my energy into this wonderful gift when I was not with them.

To Kathleen Fortini, for giving me the amazing present from Dylan Skye. A much needed boost. The Rowan Tree Foundation, for giving us a place to honor our little boy at their memorial. Deb Sheppard, my spiritual mentor, who laid the ground work that didn't make total sense until this happened. My new friends and teachers that I met on my journey to help me understand, to learn, trust and grow to help others and spread my Dylan's love and enthusiasm for life, Sarina Baptista, Suzanne Giesemann and Sue Fredrick.

Our personal trainer Animal (Brent) Brasure, who gave us an outlet for our pain and frustration and cheered us up with his impersonations.

Kelly Johnson, who led me kicking and screaming into the unfamiliar area of social media. Judith Briles and Rebecca Finkel, who helped me along my path to bringing our book into reality.

And last but not least, my ever present dog Zelda Blue Moon, who faithfully kept watch, encouraged me with licks and laughter on this book's journey.

Love to them all, Disa